Guest Spot

21 CLASSIC HITS
Playalong *for* Trumpet
BLUE BOOK

Wise Publications
part of The Music Sales Group
London/New York/Paris/Sydney/Copenhagen/Berlin/Madrid/Tokyo

Published by
Wise Publications
14/15 Berners Street, London W1T 3LJ, England.

Exclusive Distributors:
Music Sales Limited
Distribution Centre, Newmarket Road, Bury St. Edmunds,
Suffolk IP33 3YB, England.
Music Sales Pty Limited
Units 3-4, 17 Willfox Street, Condell Park,
NSW 2200, Australia.

Order No. AM978824
ISBN 1-84449-292-3
This book © Copyright 2003 by Wise Publications.

Cover photography by George Taylor.

CD mastered by Jonas Persson.
Instrumental solos by Tony Fisher.

Guest Spot

Trumpet Fingering Chart

MOUTHPIECE

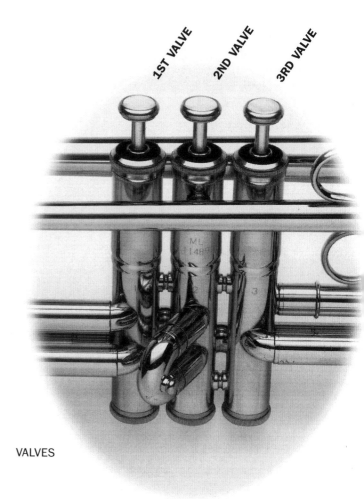

1ST VALVE 2ND VALVE 3RD VALVE

VALVES

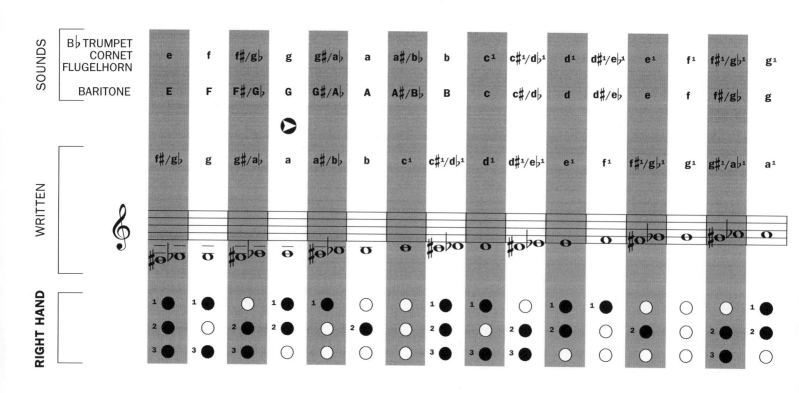

Indicates the lower limit of the best playing range

Transposition

The B♭ trumpet, cornet and flugelhorn sound a major second below the written pitch.
Rule: **Written C sounds B♭**

Written:    Sounds:

The baritone sounds a major ninth below the written pitch. Rule: **Written C sounds B♭**

Written: 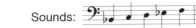   Sounds:

Pitch System

The letter names which appear at the top of the fingering chart indicate the relative octave as well as the name of each pitch, as shown below.

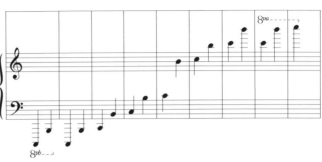

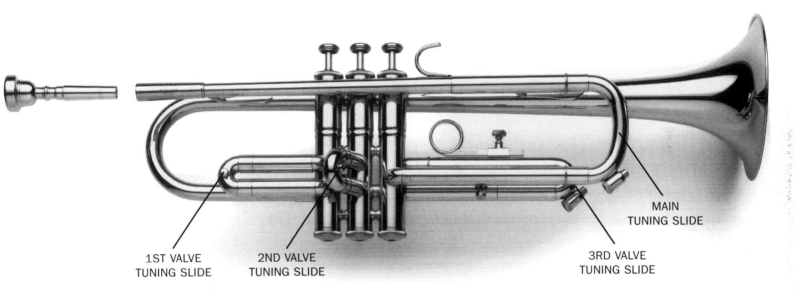

1ST VALVE TUNING SLIDE   2ND VALVE TUNING SLIDE   3RD VALVE TUNING SLIDE   MAIN TUNING SLIDE

Indicates the upper limit of the best playing range

American Pie

Words & Music by Don McLean

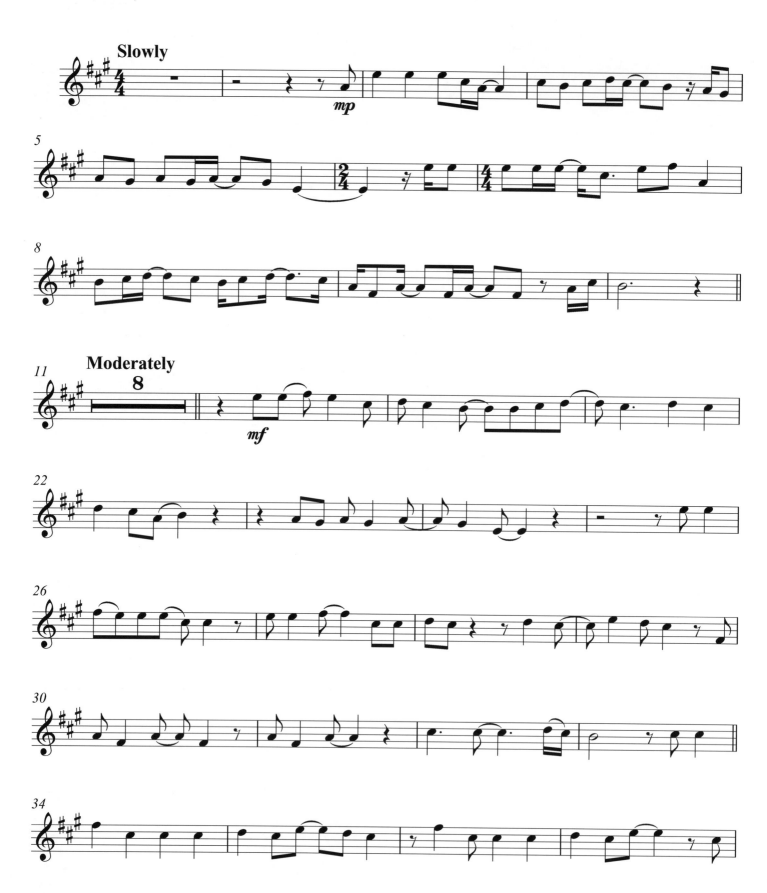

Desert Rose

Words & Music by Sting

The Girl From Ipanema (Garota De Ipanema)

Original Words by Vinicius De Moraes
Music by Antonio Carlos Jobim
English Words by Norman Gimbel

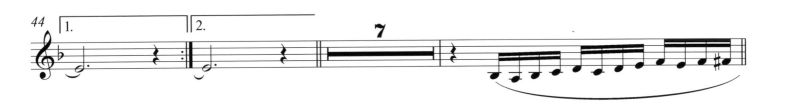

Guantanamera

Words Adaptated by Julian Orbon from a poem by José Marti
Music Adaptation by Pete Seeger & Julian Orbon

p *poco a poco cresc.*

mp

mf

dim.

rit.

mp

I Got You (I Feel Good)

Words & Music by James Brown

I Say A Little Prayer

Words by Hal David
Music by Burt Bacharach

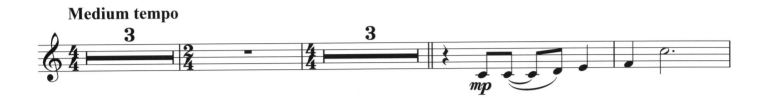

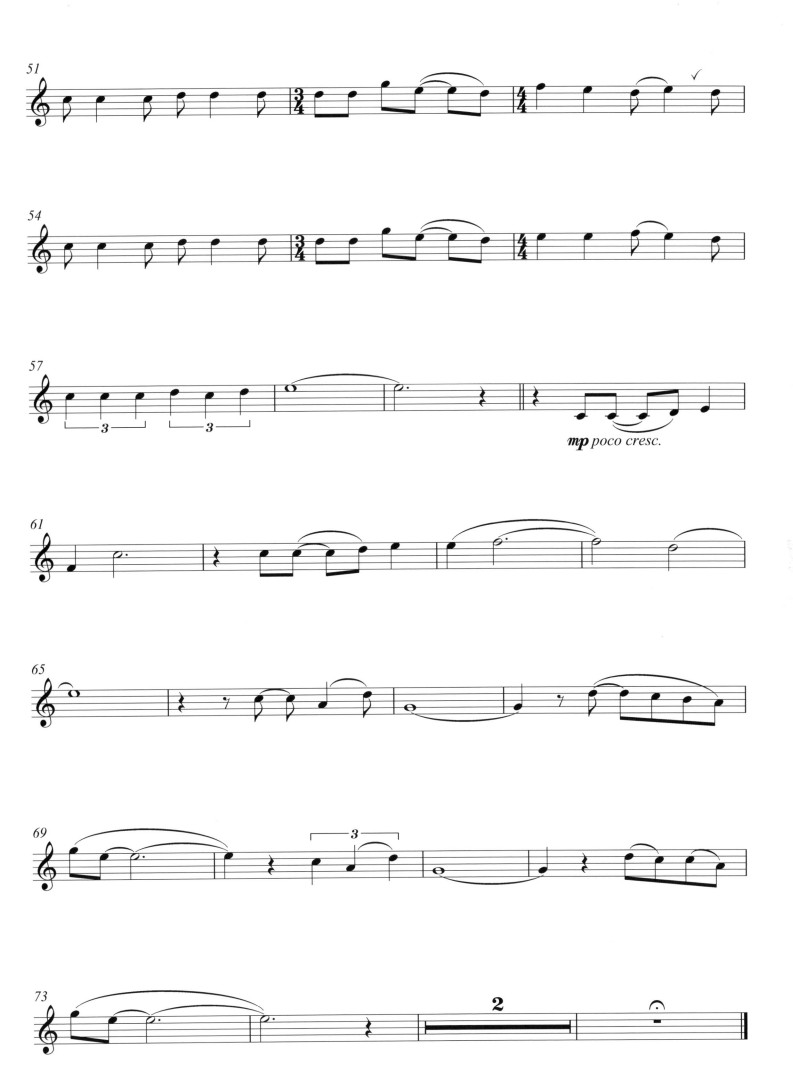

La Bamba

Traditional
Adapted & Arranged by Ritchie Valens

Moonglow

Words & Music by Will Hudson, Eddie de Lange & Irving Mills

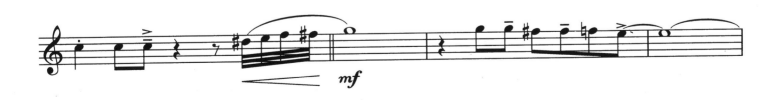

In The Midnight Hour

Words & Music by Steve Cropper & Wilson Pickett

One Note Samba (Samba De Uma Nota Só)

Original Words by Newton Mendonca
Music by Antonio Carlos Jobim
English Words by Jon Hendricks

To ⊕ Coda

D.𝄋 al Coda

⊕ **CODA**

Oye Como Va

Words & Music by Tito Puente

Pure Shores

Words & Music by William Orbit & Shaznay Lewis

Reach

Words & Music by Cathy Dennis & Andrew Todd

Rise

Words & Music by Bob Dylan, Gabrielle, Ferdy Unger-Hamilton & Ollie Dagois

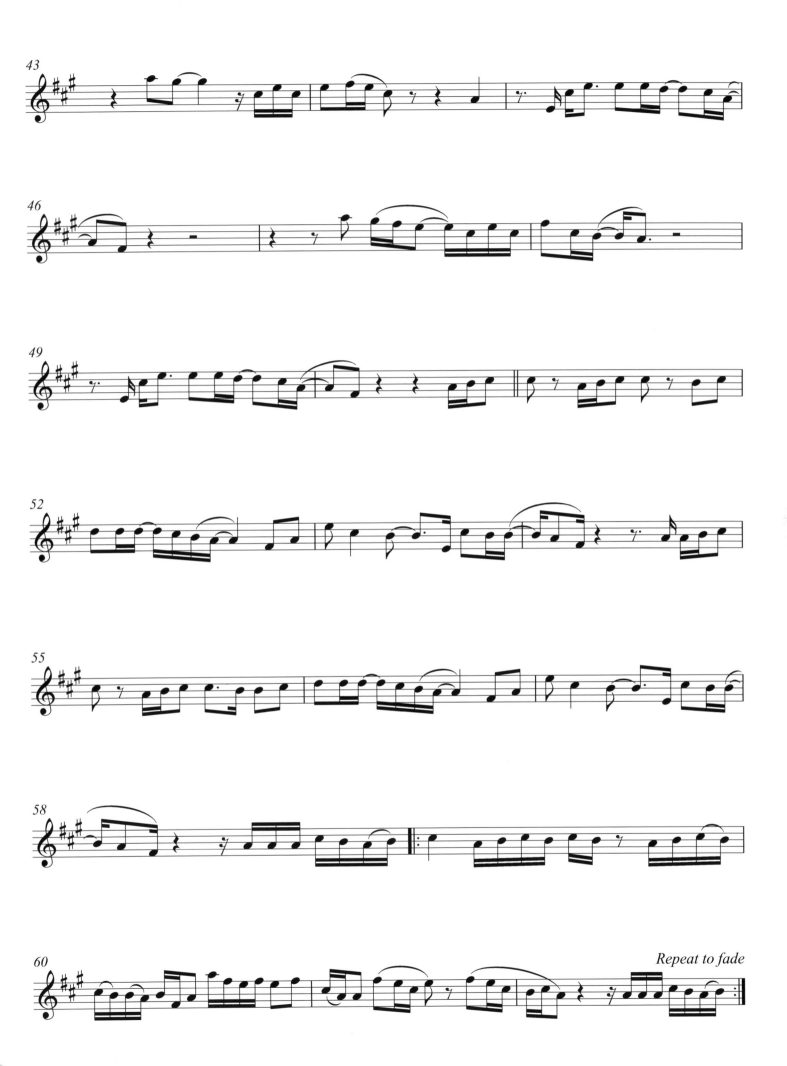

Repeat to fade

She's The One

Words & Music by Karl Wallinger

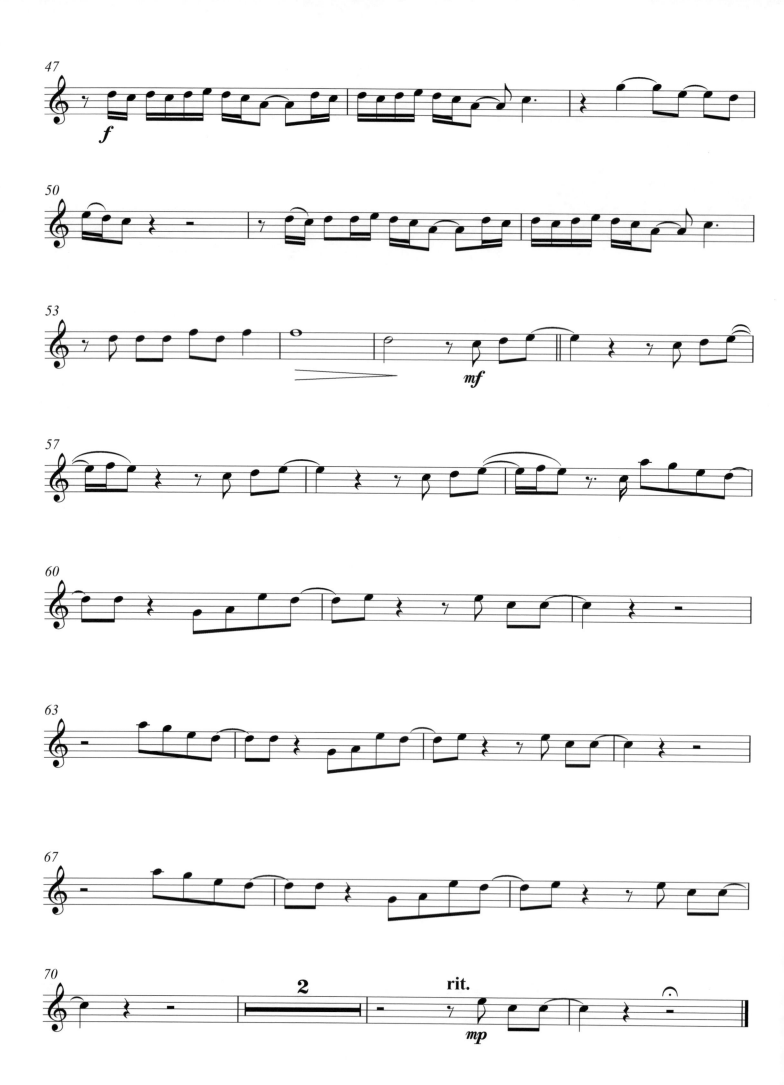

Slightly Out Of Tune (Desafinado)

Original Words by Newton Mendonca
Music by Antonio Carlos Jobim
English Words by Jon Hendricks & Jessie Cavanaugh

D.%. al Coda

CODA

rall.

(Sittin' On) The Dock Of The Bay

Words & Music by Steve Cropper & Otis Redding

Straight No Chaser

By Thelonious Monk

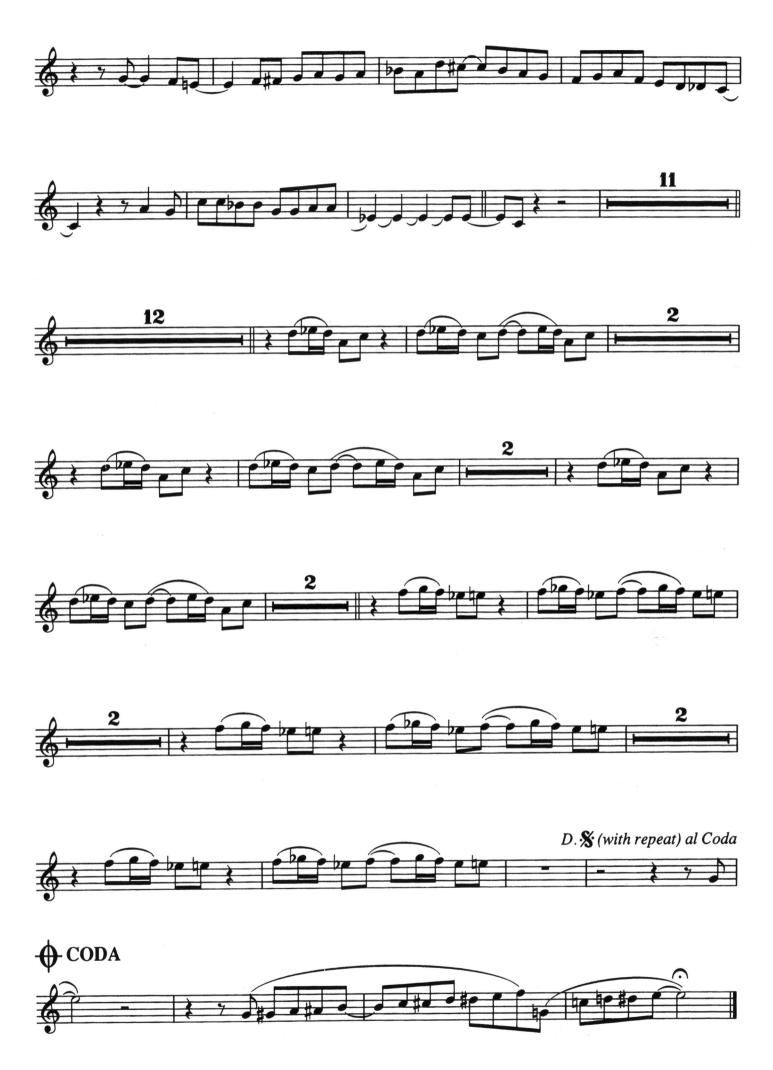

D. 𝄋 (with repeat) al Coda

CODA

Sway (Quien Sera)

Original Words & Music by Pablo Beltran Ruiz
English Words by Norman Gimbel

Stand By Me

Words & Music by Ben E. King, Jerry Leiber & Mike Stoller

Medium fast tempo

Take The 'A' Train

Words & Music by Billy Strayhorn

D.S. (with repeat) al Coda

$\oplus$ **CODA**

1. Tuning notes

2. American Pie

   (McLean) Universal/MCA Music Limited

3. Desert Rose

   (Sumner) Steerpike (Overseas) Limited

4. The Girl From Ipanema
   (Garota De Ipanema)

   (Jobim/de Moraes/Gimbel) Universal/MCA Music Limited /
   Windswept Music (London) Limited

5. Guantanamera

   (Orbon/Marti/Seeger) Harmony Music Limited

6. I Got You (I Feel Good)

   (Brown) Lark Music Limited (Carlin)

7. I Say A Little Prayer

   (Bacharach/David) Universal/MCA Music Limited /
   Windswept Music (London) Limited

8. La Bamba

   (Trad. arr. Valens) Carlin Music Corporation

9. Moonglow

   (Hudson/de Lange/Mills) Lafleur Music Limited

10. In The Midnight Hour

    (Cropper/Pickett) Carlin Music Corporation

11. One Note Samba
    (Samba De Uma Nota Só)

    (Jobim/Mendonca/Hendricks) Universal/MCA Music Limited

12. Oye Como Va

    (Puente) EMI Music Publishing (WP) Limited

13. Pure Shores

    (Orbit/Lewis) Rondor Music (London) Limited /
    Universal/MCA Music Limited / EMI Music Publishing Limited /
    Chrysalis Music Limited

14. Reach

    (Dennis/Todd) EMI Music Publishing Limited / BMG Music Publishing Limited

15. Rise

    (Dylan/Gabrielle/Unger-Hamilton/Dagois)
    Sony/ATV Music Publishing (UK) Limited / Perfect Songs Limited /
    Chrysalis Music Limited

16. She's The One

    (Wallinger) Universal Music Publishing Limited

17. Slightly Out Of Tune (Desafinado)

    (Jobim/Mendonca/Hendricks/Cavanaugh) TRO Essex Music Limited

18. (Sittin' On) The Dock Of The Bay

    (Cropper/Redding) Rondor Music (London) Limited /
    Warner/Chappell Music Limited

19. Straight No Chaser

    (Monk) Bocu Music Limited

20. Sway (Quien Sera)

    (Ruiz/Gimbel) Latin-American Music Publishing Company Limited

21. Stand By Me

    (King/Leiber/Stoller) Hornall Brothers Music Limited

22. Take The 'A' Train

    (Strayhorn) Campbell Connelly & Company Limited

---

1. Tuning notes
2. American Pie
3. Desert Rose
4. The Girl From Ipanema
   (Garota De Ipanema)
5. Guantanamera
6. I Got You (I Feel Good)
7. I Say A Little Prayer
8. La Bamba
9. Moonglow
10. In The Midnight Hour
11. One Note Samba
    (Samba De Uma Nota Só)
12. Oye Como Va
13. Pure Shores
14. Reach
15. Rise
16. She's The One
17. Slightly Out Of Tune (Desafinado)
18. (Sittin' On) The Dock Of The Bay
19. Straight No Chaser
20. Sway (Quien Sera)
21. Stand By Me
22. Take The 'A' Train

MCPS

To remove your CD from the plastic sleeve, lift the small lip on the right to break the perforated flap. Replace the disc after use for convenient storage.